THUNDERBIRDS

...DANGER ZONE

**Edited and compiled by
Alan Fennell**

RAVETTE BOOKS

Edited and compiled by Alan Fennell.

Artwork by Frank Bellamy and Graham Bleathman.

First published by Ravette Books Limited 1992.

Printed and bound for Ravette Books Limited
3 Glenside Estate, Star Road,
Partridge Green, Horsham,
West Sussex RH13 8RA
An Egmont Company
by Proost International Bookproduction, Belgium
ISBN: 1 85304 459 8

Contents

"The Trapped Spy" · **4**

This is Tracy Island · **20**

Profile: Jeff Tracy · **21**

"Operation Earthquake" · **22**

Tracy Island — Technical Data · **36**

"Tracy Island Exposed" · **38**

THUNDERBIRDS

RELAYED BY THUNDERBIRD 5

THUNDERBIRDS

ONE SPY – ONE TARGET... THE BEREZNIK STATE ZOO...

WITHIN SECONDS...

IF THIS DOESN'T START FIRST TIME... I'M A DEAD MAN!

THE SPY HEADS TOWARDS THE MOUNTAINOUS BEREZNIK–RUSSIAN BORDER...

A SHELL SMASHES INTO THE CATERPILLAR TRACK...

THE WORLD SECURITY COUNCIL, WASHINGTON, U.S.A...

WE'VE GOT TO GET 39 OUT – THE PLANS HE HAS ARE VITAL TO OUR SECURITY!

THERE'S ONLY ONE ORGANIZATION THAT CAN RESCUE BEFORE THE BEREZNIK TROOPS REACH HIM!

THAT'S THE POSITION INTERNATIONAL RESCUE! WHEN CAN YOU GET HIM OUT?

I'LL CALL YOU BACK WITH AN ANSWER, ADMIRAL!

RELAYED BY THUNDERBIRD 5

THUNDERBIRDS

DON'T WORRY, GENTLEMEN— WE'LL FORCE INTERNATIONAL RESCUE TO GET OUT AGENT 3— LEAVE THIS TO THE U.S.S.!

A U.S.S. agent has stolen plans from a Bereznik research centre. While trying to escape he is trapped in a cave tunnel. International Rescue is called in to save the man, but Jeff Tracy refuses . . .

THE BEREZNIK DICTATOR WILL HAVE TO CALL FOR INTERNATIONAL RESCUE— AND THEN...

PARACHUTED INTO BEREZNIK BY NIGHT, THE U.S.S. AGENTS CARRY OUT THEIR INSTRUCTIONS AND WAIT. THEN...

THERE SHE IS...LET HER GET RIGHT INTO THE BUILDING!

NO

A SECOND EXPLOSION SMASHES THE SHEATH CONTROL...

OPEN THE SHEATH! OPEN IT— THE GAS ALARM HAS SOUNDED!

SHEATH CONTROLS ARE JAMMED— WE CAN NEVER RELEASE IT!

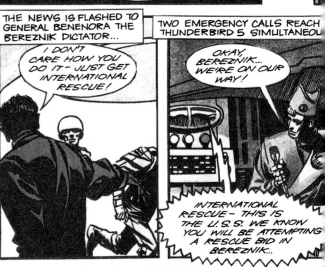

THE NEWS IS FLASHED TO GENERAL BENENORA THE BEREZNIK DICTATOR...

I DON'T CARE HOW YOU DO IT— JUST GET INTERNATIONAL RESCUE!

TWO EMERGENCY CALLS REACH THUNDERBIRD 5 SIMULTANEOU

OKAY, BEREZNIK... WE'RE ON OUR WAY!

INTERNATIONAL RESCUE— THIS IS THE U.S.S. WE KNOW YOU WILL BE ATTEMPTING A RESCUE BID IN BEREZNIK...

"Travel underwater to Bereznik, Gordon — and get General Benenora to agree to my plan."

THUNDERBIRD 4 TO BASE! APPROACHING BEREZNIK!

"After you've dropped Gordon, return home to base and pick up the Mole and Pod 3, Virgil,—then head for the Bereznik-Russian border. As soon as Benenora agrees, you can go into action . . ."

WORLD AIR FORCE BASE OKINAWA TO WASHINGTON. INTERNATIONAL RESCUE CRAFT SIGHTED... ORDERING FIGHTERS TO PURSUE...

S.S. CHIEF CALLS TWO AGENTS TO HIS OFFICE...

THIS IS THE BEREZNIK RESEARCH CENTRE. KATANIA BENENORA, DAUGHTER OF THE BEREZNIK DICTATOR, IS DUE TO VISIT THE ADMINISTRATION BUILDING TOMORROW!

NOW, IF THIS BUILDING IS ATTACKED A PROTECTIVE FOUR FEET THICK STEEL SHIELD RISES FROM THE GROUND.

POISON GAS TIME BOMBS WILL BE PLACED IN THAT BUILDING. ONCE KATANIA IS INSIDE, MY DEPARTMENT WILL CAUSE THE SHIELD TO BE BROUGHT UP AND JAMMED IN POSITION!

THE EXPLOSION OPERATES THE DEFENCE CONTROL...

STAND BY FOR PHASE TWO... NOW!

THUNDERBIRD 5

UNLESS OUR AGENT IS ALSO RESCUED, WE WILL SHOOT DOWN ANY CRAFT CROSSING THE BEREZNIK BORDER.

JOHN CALLS UP BASE...

NEITHER SIDE WILL GIVE WAY. WHAT ARE WE GOING TO DO, FATHER?

DO? RESCUE THEM BOTH, OF COURSE!

VIRGIL, TAKE THUNDERBIRD 4 TO THE BALTIC. GORDON CAN CARRY ON FROM THERE.

YES, FATHER.

SEEK OUT TARGET AND FOLLOW— IF IT HEADS FOR BEREZNIK SHOOT IT DOWN!

FRANK BELLAMY

THUNDERBIRD 2

WORLD AIR FORCE FIGHTERS ON MY TAIL, FATHER—I'D BE HAPPIER IF YOU INFORMED THE U.S.S. WE'RE GOING TO RESCUE THEIR MAN!

I CAN'T, VIRGIL—IF GENERAL BERENORA KNEW WE WERE GONNA RESCUE THE U.S.S. AGENT BEFORE GORDON TELLS HIM MY PLAN, HE'D LET HIS DAUGHTER DIE RATHER THAN LET US HELP!

AT THAT MOMENT, IN BEREZNIK'S MAIN HARBOUR...

THUNDERBIRD 4 TO BASE! HAVE ARRIVED IN BEREZNIK!

'S A PITY 'LL NEVER VER IT! TAKE TO THE CELLS— D BRING BACK S UNIFORM.

YOU CAN'T DO THIS! I MUST SEE THE GENERAL!

SEND ME OUR BEST MAN! I HAVE A JOB FOR HIM!

YES—WHEN MY INTERNATIONAL RESCUE MAN ASSASSINATES OUR BELOVED GENERAL—I WILL BE MADE PRESIDENT AND INTERNATIONAL RESCUE WILL BE BLAMED!

COME BACK! DON'T YOU REALIZE THIS IS A MATTER OF LIFE AND DEATH?

OF COURSE WE DO—THE GENERAL'S DEATH!

AT THAT MOMENT, AT THE BEREZNIK RESEARCH CENTRE WHERE KATANIA IS TRAPPED...

INTERNATIONAL RESCUE MAN TO SEE GENERAL BERENORA!

NATIONAL E WORLD I AM HEADING — AND WILL ATTACKED!

IT'S NO USE, GENERAL! THE LASER IS MAKING NO IMPRESSION!

THERE MUST BE A WAY—THAT GAS WILL FILL THE BUILDING IN ANOTHER HOUR, AND MY DAUGHTER IS INSIDE!

INTERNATIONAL RESCUE TO GENERAL BERENORA! COME IN, PLEASE!

THERE'S NO REPLY FROM BEREZNIK, FATHER—AND TIME'S RUNNING OUT!

IT'S RUNNING OUT FOR EVERYONE, SCOTT—THE U.S.S. AGENT TRAPPED IN HIS CAVE—FOR KATANIA BERENORA...

THE ASSASSIN MOVES FORWARD...

...AND FOR US!

THUNDERBIRDS

A U.S.S. agent, who has stolen secret plans from Bereznik is now trapped in a cave on the Russian-Bereznik border . . .

At Bere... ter cove... fillin... gas

STEADY! DON'T RUSH IT! AS SOON AS THAT OFFICER MOVES...

GENERAL! INTERNATIONAL RESCUE ARE CALLING YOU!

. WELL, ARE YOU COMING OR NOT?

I'LL BE WITH YOU IN MINUTES, GENERAL - BUT BE ON THE LOOK OUT- SOMEONE WEARING AN INTERNATIONAL RESCUE UNIFORM IS OUT TO ASSASSINATE YOU!

THUNDERBIRD 2 QUICKLY ARRIVES AT THE MOUNTAINS WHERE THE AGENT IS TRAPPED...

WE SHOULD HAVE THE AG... OUT IN HALF AN HOUR!

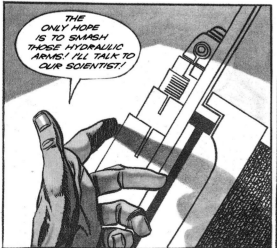

THE ONLY HOPE IS TO SMASH THOSE HYDRAULIC ARMS! I'LL TALK TO OUR SCIENTIST!

AS I SEE IT, SCOTT - THE SHEATH IS SO BIG IT WILL BE A LITTLE FLEXIBLE! TWO HYDRAULIC JACKS COULD BEND IN THE SHEATH MAKING A SMALL GAP BETWEEN IT AND THE TRENCH LINING!

I GET IT, BRAINS - THEN I SLIP INTO THE TRENCH AND DESTROY THE HYDRAULIC ARMS!

HALF A DOZEN HYDRAULIC JACKS, GENERAL!

YOU HEARD HIM!

Gordon Tracy tries to contact the dictator to offer help, but is caught by Colonel Tobolsk—head of the Bereznik secret police. Tobolsk sees his chance for power and one of his men uses Gordon's uniform as a guise in order to get near enough to kill the dictator . . .

AWARE OF THE ASSASSINATION PLOT SCOTT SPEEDS THUNDERBIRD 1 TOWARDS BEREZNIK...

INTERNATIONAL RESCUE TO GENERAL BERENORA! COME IN, PLEASE!

VIRGIL IN THUNDERBIRD 2, IS LISTENING INTO SCOTT'S MESSAGES...

ALL RIGHT, INTERNATIONAL RESCUE, BUT IF YOU TRICK ME...

OKAY, SCOTT—I HEARD THE GENERAL! I'M GOING TO GET THE AGENT OUT!

WE CAN'T BURROW UNDER THE SHEATH BECAUSE ITS TRENCH IS ALSO STEEL LINED!

HOW IS IT LOWERED AND RAISED?

MEANWHILE, THUNDERBIRD 1 ARRIVES AT THE STEEL SHEATHED BUILDING...

'S ING- GAP'S ENING!

GET READY... THE JACKS WON'T LAST FOR LONG!

ONE OF THE JACKS IS ALREADY SLIPPING...

... AND WHEN IT GOES, THE SHEATH WILL SNAP BACK INTO POSITION, SLICING OFF THE GAP...

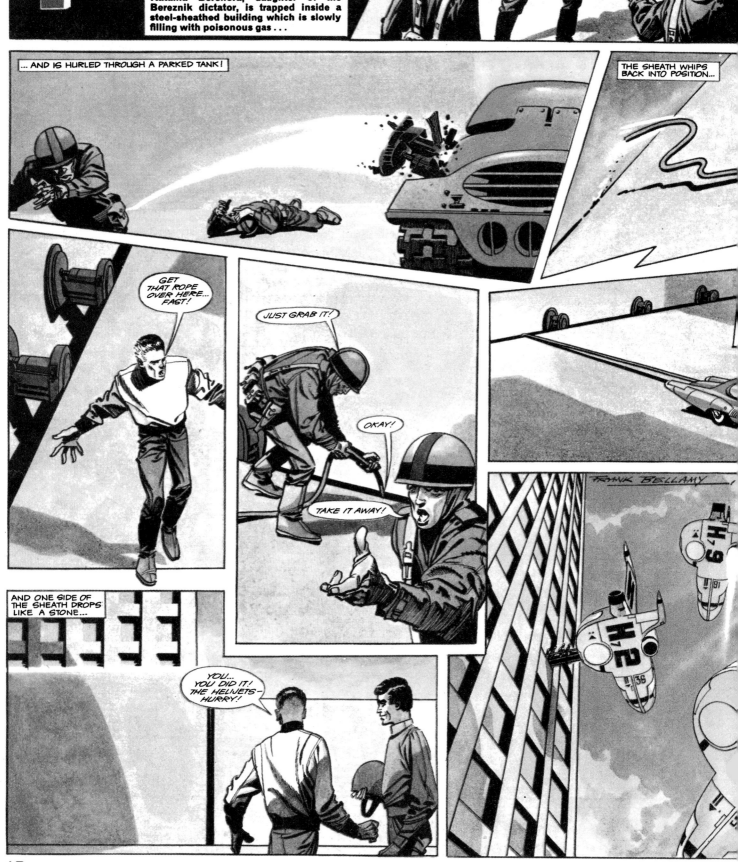

THUNDERBIRDS

While Scott is rescuing Katania Berenora from a Bereznik research building, Virgil hits a snag in his attempted rescue of a U.S.S. agent...

BUT...

I'M SORRY, BUT THE TRAITOR TOBOLSK HOLDS YOUR MAN. IF I SEND TROOPS HE WILL KILL HIM!

OKAY GENERAL — WHERE'S THE ASSASSIN WHO TRIED TO KILL YOU?

THE MAN IS DRAGGED FORWARD...

WHERE'S TOBOLSK KEEPING THE MEMBER OF OUR ORGANISATION?

TELL HIM AND YOU LIVE!

I'LL TELL! I'LL TELL!

SECONDS

HE'S IN THE DUNGEON CELLS — THIS ONE! HIS GRILL WINDOW FACES NORTH!

I'M OVERHEAD, GORDON... COMING IN!

OPEN FIRE YOU FOOLS! SHOOT!

YOU DID IT, SCOTT!

STAND BY — HERE COMES THE LINE!

14

15

THUNDERBIRDS

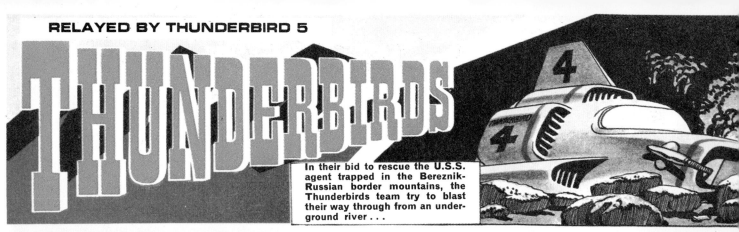

In their bid to rescue the U.S.S. agent trapped in the Bereznik-Russian border mountains, the Thunderbirds team try to blast their way through from an underground river . . .

I'M THROUGH!

THANK THE STARS! I'D ALMOST GIVEN UP HOPE UNTIL I HEARD THAT BANG...

CALM DOWN, FELLER—WE'RE NOT OUT YET!

LO... SO... LET'S MO...

THIS IS IT! TAKE A DEEP BREATH!

MIRACULOUSLY MEN AND MACHINE SURVIVE THE SAVAGE JOURNEY...

CALM RETURNS, AND WITH IT A UNIT OF WORLD GOVERNMENT TROOPS...

THE BEREZNIK PAPERS, WHERE ARE THEY?

I DESTROYED THEM!

18

19

THIS IS Tracy Island

To the outside world, Tracy Island is one of several atolls owned by multi-millionaire industrialist and space shuttle manufacturer Jeff Tracy.

Jeff Tracy's two man jet is used primarily for collecting supplies: at speeds in excess of 2000mph, the Australian mainland is less than half an hour away.

Tracy House. A large two storey building in which Jeff lives with his family, Kyrano and Tin Tin. Brains, the young scientist who designed the Thunderbird craft also has quarters in the house.

Left: The Cliff House overlooks the island's runway and jetty beyond, while the Round House (below) is used primarily for guests if all the rooms at the main house are full. They conceal hangars to Thunderbird 2 and 3 respectively.

As well as his private aircraft, Jeff Tracy owns a number of boats, including small yachts and motor launches. Also docked at the island is Lucille, a luxury cruiser named after Jeff's late wife.

PROFILE ON JEFF TRACY

The founder of International Rescue, Jeff Tracy started life on a Kansas wheat farm. His father was a combine harvest driver and his mechanical vocation possibly influenced young Jeff to become interested in machinery.

His military service was spent with the U.S. Air Force, and from the ranks he rose to a colonel before transferring to Space Agency projects.

Instantly he was a success as an astronaut and has the distinction of being chosen for the Moon flight that celebrated the arrival of the twenty-first century. Jeff built up a highly profitable company building shuttles and space related hardware. Then tragedy struck the Tracy household. His wife, Lucille, died prematurely and the raising of five robust and healthy sons became Jeff's first duty.

Caring for a family and building up a business at the same time wasn't easy for Jeff, but his tremendous capacity for work carried him through to success.

He went into civil and construction engineering and became, in a short space of time, one of the richest men in the world. His humanity towards people in general prompted the conception of International Rescue, and from his plans and spirit of enterprise, the organisation took shape and became a reality.

Jeff is intelligent, kindly and has a sense of humour but when the situation demands, he can be decisive and occasionally very stern.

Date of Birth: January 2nd.

"OPERATION EARTHQUAKE".

RELAYED BY THUNDERBIRD 5

THUNDERBIRDS

Moscow, the morning of May 8th, 2067 . . .

IMMEDIATELY THE OUTSIDE WORLD KNOWS OF THE DISASTER, OPERATION RESCUE SWINGS INTO ACTION...

AMONG THE ORGANI? WHO RUSH TO THE STRICKEN CITY IS INTERNATIONAL RES

THUNDERBIRD 2'S POD COMES INTO ACTION...

FIRE UNDER CONTROL!

RETURN TO POD, VIRGIL! GORDON - THERE'S A HU MOUND OF RUBBLE IN SQUARE - CLEAR IT!

WELL DONE, BOYS - YOU'VE ALL WORKED HARD!

ALL EYES FOCUS ON BRAINS, AND...

OH, NOT THE RESCUE, BUT THE EARTHQUAKE! WHY WASN'T THERE ANY PRE-WARNING?

THAT'S A POINT, BRAINS - SCIENTISTS CAN TELL AT LEAST TWENTY-FOUR HOURS IN ADVANCE WHEN AND WHERE AN EARTHQUAKE'S GOING TO HIT!

BUT WAS IT NECESSARY?

WHAT?

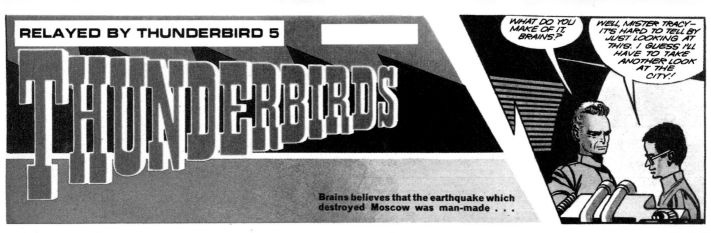

THUNDERBIRDS

Brains believes that the earthquake which destroyed Moscow was man-made . . .

WHAT DO YOU MAKE OF IT, BRAINS?

WELL, MISTER TRACY— IT'S HARD TO TELL BY JUST LOOKING AT THIS. I GUESS I'LL HAVE TO TAKE ANOTHER LOOK AT THE CITY!

WE WON'T... ER... FIND ANYTHING ON THE SURFACE, VIRGIL— SO WE'LL START WITH THE... ER... MOLE!

THE MOLE EDGES FORWARD, AND THEN...

THIS IS IT, VIRGIL— LOOK AT THE EXPLOSION MARKS IN THE ROOF... AND LOOK, MACHINE TRACKS!

ANY NEWS FROM BRAINS, SCOTT?

YES, FATHER— THEY'VE FOUND SOME SORT OF CAVERN AND MACHINE TRACKS WHICH THEY'RE FOLLOWING THROUGH!

HOLD TIGHT, BRAINS— I'M BACKING UP!

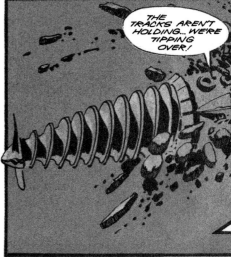

THE TRACKS AREN'T HOLDING... WE'RE TIPPING OVER!

THUNDERBIRDS

Virgil and Brains are in the Mole following the tracks of a giant machine which a gang of crooks are using to cause earthquakes. Suddenly the Mole bores through an undersea cliff . . .

OKAY, VIRGIL, I'LL TELL FATHER. DON'T WORRY, GORDON WILL SOON GET YOU OUT!

FROM WHAT JOHN SAYS THEY'RE ALONG THE WHITE SEA AREA!

A J THUNL SC

I STIL SHOU RE

A HA FAIL? TO FL AND RETU

HOW'S IT GOING, VIRGIL?

NOT TOO GOOD, FATHER!

THE FALL HAS FRACTURED ONE OF THE OXYGEN FEEDS—WE'RE GETTING KINDA SHORT OF BREATH!

AT THAT MOMENT...

VIRGIL! ARE YOU RECEIVING ME? IT'S SCOTT.

YOU'VE BROUGHT THUNDERBIRD 4.?

NOT YET, VIRGIL—BUT IT'S ON ITS WAY! HAVE YOU TRIED THE ESCAPE UNIT?

IT'S NO USE, SCOTT, WE'RE UPSIDE DO AND CAN'T MOVE!

FRANK BELLAMY

RELAYED BY THUNDERBIRD 5

THUNDERBIRDS

The Mole is trapped upside down on the White Sea. In a desperate attem[pt to save] the craft, Thunderbird 1 closes in .

MOLE

YOU'VE DONE IT, SCOTT! YOU'VE DONE IT!

THEN GET OUT OF THERE FAST!

AND SO...

THAT'S ABOUT IT!

BUT AS THUNDERBIRD 2 PICKS UP THE POD...

BASE TO THUNDERBIRD 1 AND THUNDERBIRD 2! EARTHQUAKE AT MONTREAL, CANADA. PROCEED TO DANGER ZONE!

THE INTERNATIONAL RESCUE TEAM ARE QUICKLY IN ACTION...

SCOTT STARTS OFF IN THUNDERBIRD 1 AND LOWERS THE X-RAY SCANNER...

BRAINS! I'VE GOT SOMETHING!

SWITCH TO THE X-RAY VIDEO, SCOTT!

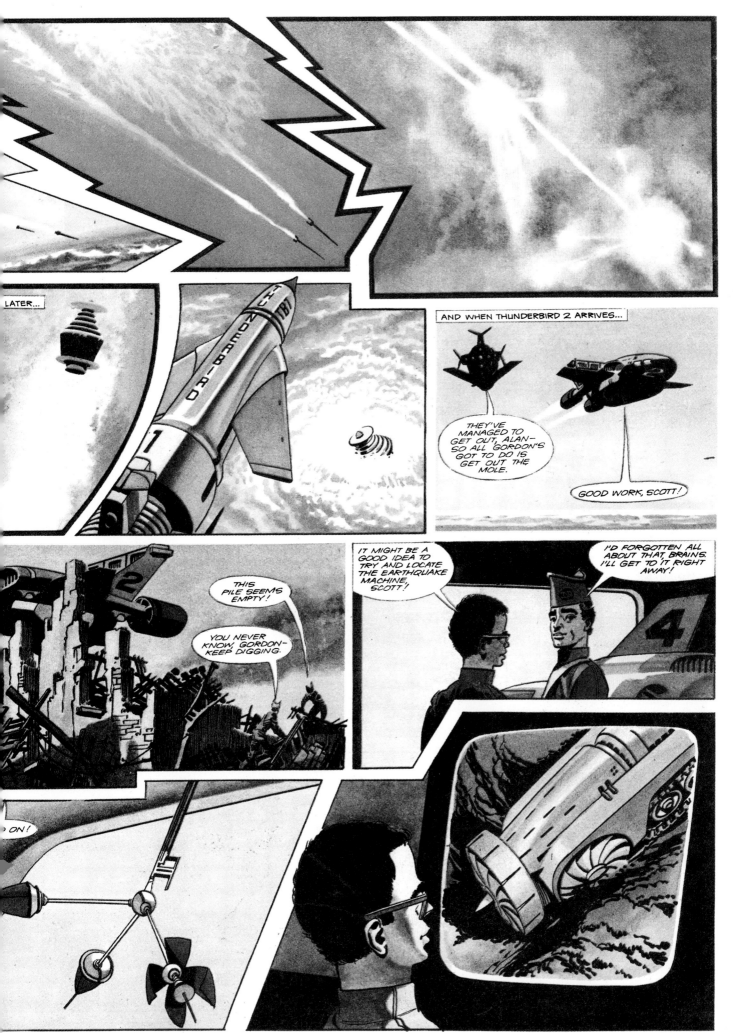

LATER...

AND WHEN THUNDERBIRD 2 ARRIVES...

THEY'VE MANAGED TO GET OUT, ALAN—SO ALL GORDON'S GOT TO DO IS GET OUT THE MOLE.

GOOD WORK, SCOTT!

THIS PILE SEEMS EMPTY!

YOU NEVER KNOW, GORDON— KEEP DIGGING.

IT MIGHT BE A GOOD IDEA TO TRY AND LOCATE THE EARTHQUAKE MACHINE, SCOTT!

I'D FORGOTTEN ALL ABOUT THAT, BRAINS. I'LL GET TO IT RIGHT AWAY!

ON!

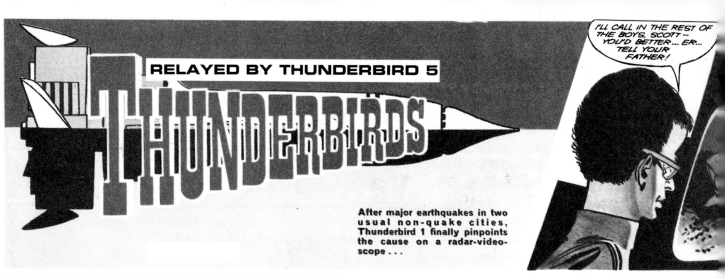

RELAYED BY THUNDERBIRD 5

THUNDERBIRDS

I'LL CALL IN THE REST OF THE BOYS, SCOTT — YOU'D BETTER... ER... TELL YOUR FATHER!

After major earthquakes in two usual non-quake cities, Thunderbird 1 finally pinpoints the cause on a radar-video-scope...

IT'S JUST ENTERED THE OCEAN — BRING UP THUNDERBIRD 4 — I'LL TRACK IT ON SONASOUND UNTIL YOU ARRIVE!

HEADING NORTH, NORTH-EAST!

WOW! WHAT A SIZE! BUT WHERE'S IT GOING?

SUDDENLY...

WHAT A HIDEOUT — WE'LL NEED THE MOLE, BRAINS!

FRANK BELLAMY

HOW'S THE REPAIRS?

TWO MINUTES, SCOTT — THEN WE'RE READY TO GO!

GET READY!

YOU'RE ALL UNDER ARREST!

WELL, IT'S NOT OUR JOB TO CATCH CROOKS, NO MATTER HOW BAD THEY ARE, SCOTT!

BUT AS THIS BUNCH ARE CAUSING DISASTERS, AND PREVENTION IS BETTER THAN CURE—I GUESS YOU'D BETTER GET THEM!

F.A.B., FATHER!

WHILE THUNDERBIRD 1 TRACKS THE MACHINE, THE REST OF THE INTERNATIONAL RESCUE TEAM FOLLOW...

THE TRAIL LEADS TO THE ROCKY COAST OF NEWFOUNDLAND...

AS THE MOLE IS PUT ASHORE, BIRD 4 IS PICKED UP...

...TRAIGHT ...ALAN!

RIGHT, STAND BACK!

BUT...

THAT MEANS YOU, TOO, MISTER!

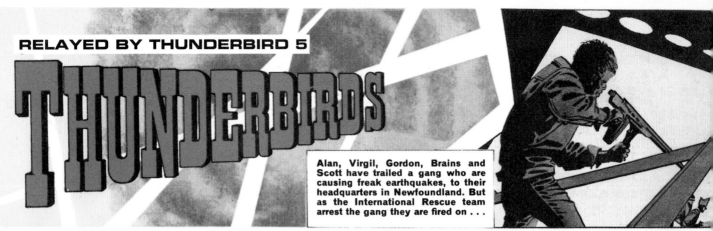

RELAYED BY THUNDERBIRD 5

THUNDERBIRDS

Alan, Virgil, Gordon, Brains and Scott have trailed a gang who are causing freak earthquakes, to their headquarters in Newfoundland. But as the International Rescue team arrest the gang they are fired on . . .

BUT AS THE MOLE ROLLS FORWARD...

GET SOMEONE IN THE DIGGER! I'M GOING TO LOAD THE GOLD ON TO A TRUCK— JUST IN CASE WE HAVE TO MAKE A RUN FOR IT!

PROTECTED BY THE MOLE, SCOTT RACES FOR THE CHAIN HANGING FROM THE GALLERY...

IF THEY GET THAT MACHINE GOING, WE'RE IN TROUBLE!

THE DIGGERS CLASH...

...AND BRAINS FIRES THE OIL DRUMS...

AND THEN...

THE TWO MACHINE IN A FURY OF DE

TRACY ISLAND

TRACY ISLAND DATA
1. The Round House, a sound and blast proof building concealing Thunderbird 3's launch bay, 2. Maintenance bays for TB3 and blast duct, 3. Underground pen for pleasure boats, leading to sea, 4. Tunnel connecting Tracy House to pen, 5. Tracy House, with access to TB1's hangar, 6. TB1's hangar, through which the launch chute of TB2 passes, 7. Access from lounge to TB2's launch chute, 8. Access from Tracy House to inspection monorail, 9. Retractable swimming pool above TB1's launch bay, 10. Air conditioning system serving all underground installations, 11. Water and sewage system, 12. Shaft from Tracy House giving access to 13, 13. Access tunnel for trolley leading to TB3's launch bay, 14. Access to TB2's Pod vehicle maintenance bay, exited in 15, 15. Access tunnel to TB3, 16. Monorail connects launch bays, boat pen, laboratories and power house with Tracy House, 17. Pod vehicle maintenance bay, 18. Pods on conveyor belt. Some vehicles are permanently stored in the Pods, such as Thunderbird 4, 19. Launch chute to TB2, 20. Access from Pod vehicle bay to laboratories, 21. Inspection tunnel, leading from 22, 22. Atomic power plant, 23. Blast duct from TB1 launch bay, 24. Access tunnel running parallel to monorail connecting laboratory and power house, 25. Sewerage and atomic waste treatment plant, 26. Emergency power house, 27. Two floor laboratory, 28. Heavy duty equipment test bay, housing heavy lifting gear, 29. Hangar for Jeff Tracy's jet, 30. Water filtration and purification plant, 31. Access tunnel from secondary Pod bay to laboratory, 32. Secondary Pod vehicle bay, 33. Pod conveyor belt, 34. TB2 maintenance equipment bay, 35. TB2 launch bay, 36. Cliff House, 37. Drawbridge covers Cliff Door trench allowing smooth access to runway, 38. Cliff Door, 39. Hydraulic systems for Cliff Door and Drawbridge.

RELAYED BY THUNDERBIRD 5

THUNDERBIRDS

WORLD NEWS
THUNDERBIRD HIDEOUT!
THIS IS THE INTERNATIONAL RESCUE TEAM

The Hood crashes a jet aircraft on Thunderbird 2's hangar, and photographs the area. International Rescue's base is revealed!

I WANT A COMPLETE WOODEN MOCK-UP OF THUNDERBIRD 2 BUILT ON THE RUNWAY!

BRAINS, CLEAR THE PODS FROM T82'S HANGER!

AS TIN-TIN, JOHN, GORDON AND BRAINS HURRY ABOUT THEIR JOBS, JEFF CALLS UP LADY PENELOPE...

SATURDAY WILL BRING THE BIGGEST TOURIST CROWD, PENNY. THAT'S WHEN I WANT YOU TO FAKE THE DISASTER!

LEAVE IT TO ME, JEFF, AND GOOD LUCK WITH BILL McQUIRE OF WORLD TELEVISION.

JEFF MAKES HIS SECOND CALL...

GLAD TO HELP OUT, JEFF, IT'S BEEN A LONG TIME SINCE YOU LAST CALLED ON ME.

THANKS, BILL. IF YOU GET THE CAMERA CREW OVER HERE AT FIVE TONIGHT WE'LL BE READY!

AND SO...

WORLD TELEVISION HAS FLOWN ITS CAMERAS TO THE ISLAND TO INVESTIGATE TODAY'S STARTLING CLAIM THAT IT IS THE HOME OF INTERNATIONAL RESCUE!

THE WORLD WIDE TELECAST IS BEING WATCHED BY THE HOOD...

THEY MAY FOOL THE WORLD, BUT NOT THE HOOD! I WILL JOIN THE SIGHTSEERS AND EXPOSE THEIR MACHINES FOR ALL TO SEE!

I STILL DON'T SEE 'OW WE'RE GOING TO 'ELP MISTER TRACY, M'LADY?

IT'S SIMPLE, PARKER - THUNDERBIRDS ONE AND TWO ARE IN SPACE WITH THUNDERBIRD 5.

LONDON

FRANK BELLAMY

THE DOOR CLANGS SHUT, BUT...

ALL RIGHT, BOYS - COME AND GET PARKER - HE'S LOCKED IN THE BANK OF ENGLAND VAULTS!

WHAT? OH, NO! WE HAVEN'T GOT THE MOLE! IT'S BACK AT BASE!

WE MUST HAVE THE MOLE, FATHER! LADY PENELOPE HAS LOCKED PARKER IN THE VAULT OF THE BANK OF ENGLAND!

OKAY, SCOTT—BUT WE NEED TIME!

THE ISLAND'S CRAWLING WITH SIGHTSEERS — YOU CAN'T PICK UP ANYTHING WHILE THEY ARE HERE.

CLEAR THE ISLAND, BRAINS— TELL THE PEOPLE WE'VE HAD A FIVE HOUR WARNING OF A TYPHOON.

RIGHT, MR. TRACY!

...OSE EYES...

I... I CAN'T RESIST!

SUDDENLY, KYRANO ENTERS...

YOU!

YES, KYRANO— MY HALF-BROTHER!

GORDON SEIZES HIS OPPORTUNITY...

...HILE VIRGIL AND SCOTT ...AY FOR TIME, JOHN ...D GORDON CLEAR ...ACY ISLAND...

WE'RE SORRY, FOLKS — BUT A TYPHOON WILL BE HERE IN FIVE HOURS — YOU MUST LEAVE NOW!

... AND ONCE THE LAST BOAT HAS GONE...

GET THAT MOCK-UP OFF THE RUNWAY — VIRGIL WILL BE HERE IN FIVE MINUTES!

FRANK BELLAMY

RIGHT, BRAINS— GET THE MEMORY ERASER WORKING AND LET'S GET THIS GUY OFF THE ISLAND!

YES, MISTER TRACY!

WAIT— ONE LAST WORD!

THE MOLE IS MINED... IT WILL EXPLODE IN ONE MINUTE!

THUNDERBIRDS

The Hood has exposed the headquarters of the Thunderbird team to the world. But Jeff Tracy has organised a cover-up operation making Tracy Island an amusement park. Parker has been locked in the vaults of the bank of England. Thunderbirds 1 and 2 speed to the rescue but . . .

MY FREEDOM, MR. TRACY - AND I WILL SAVE THUNDERBIRD 2!

YOU'RE BLUFFING!

AM I? TH DIGGER M WILL EXPL IN TWO MINUTES.

SWITCH OFF!

HELP ME GET HIM INTO MY AIRCRAFT, GORDON - BRAINS AND I WILL DUMP HIM ON THE MAINLAND.

AND SO...

HOW MUCH WILL HE FAIL TO REMEMBER, BRAINS?

ER... EVERYTHING THAT'S HAPPENED OVER THE LAST WEEK MR. TRACY. IT WILL ALL... ER... BE LIKE A DREAM TO HIM.

MEANWHILE...

VIRGIL! THIS IS SCOTT! WHAT'S HAPPENED TO YOU!

SORRY SCOTT - JUST A SLIGHT HOLD-UP!

YOU FINK MATE GETTIN IN TH VAL

PARKER IS RELEASED...

JOLLY GOOD SHOW, WHAT, PENNY? BUT I SAY, WHO'S GOING TO PAY FOR ALL THIS DAMAGE, OLE GIRL?

IT'S ALL BEEN TAKEN CARE OF, SIR WILLIAM - I THINK THIS SHOULD COVER THE COST!

READY, M'LADY!

PARK WHAT YOU G HIDDE UNDER COA

WELL, M'LADY, I DON'T WANT TO BOAST!

ALSO AVAILABLE IN THIS SERIES:

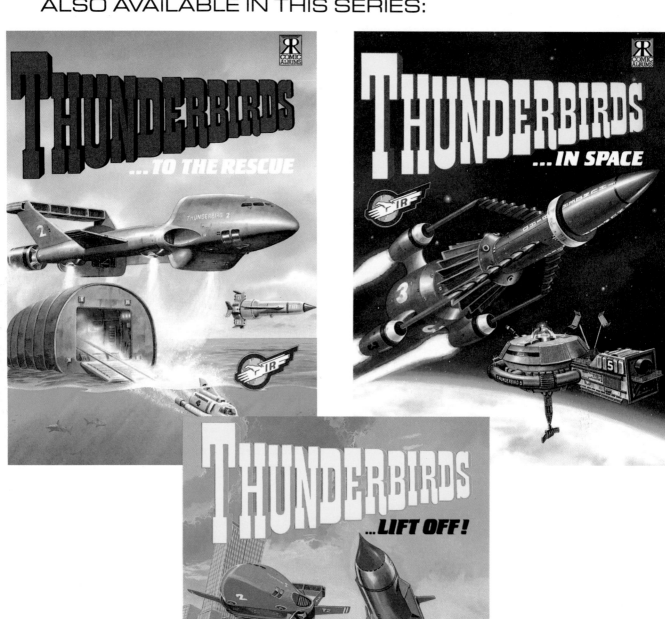

Further exciting adventures of International Rescue's Thunderbirds team and machines.